# Whole Body Reset Diet Recipes

## Easy and Delicious Recipes To Help you Lose Weight in your Midlife and Beyond.

By Stephanie Smith

**Disclaimer:**

The information provided in this book is designed to provide helpful information on the subjects discussed. The publisher and author are not responsible for any specific health or allergy needs that may require medical supervision and are not liable for any damages or negative consequences from any treatment, action, application or preparation, to any person reading or following the information in this book.

# Contents

## Introduction

The Whole Body Reset by Stephen Perrine is the first program written specifically for people at midlife who want to stay lean, active and strong for decades to come. The reason for this program is because our bodies change with age, and the way we eat needs to change in response.

Basically, This Weight-loss Program gives you the tools you need to turn back the clock and reclaim your physique, your health, and your life. This Plan uses the protein timing to achieve its goal, what this entails is that you have to eat protein in the proper amounts throughout the day. This will help trigger older bodies to say NO to fat gain and hold on to lean muscle tissue. This method, coupled with plenty of minerals and vitamins, healthy fats and fiber, can help people at midlife reshape their bodies and ultimately, their lives.

This whole body reset plan isn't low-carb or low-fat, doesn't require periods of food restriction or calorie counting, and doesn't eliminate any particular food category. However, once you know how to do it and integrate it into your daily life, it can stop, and even reverse, age-related weight gain and muscle loss. It can even significantly reduce your risk of many of the chronic diseases of aging like, hypertension, Arthritis, Diabetes, depression, Alzheimer Disease and Dementia etc. Thereby, enhancing the overall health of both your body and your brain.

# List of Foods To Eat in This Program

**PROTEIN**

**Unlike the case with carbohydrates and fats, your body is not very good at storing protein, so you have to get small hits of it throughout the day. Studies show that people who eat small amounts of protein with each meal are leaner than those who don't.**

**List of Proteins**

**Egg and egg whites (in mod-eration)**

**lean meat**

**seafood**

**Fish and shellfish**

**poultry**

**Mixtures of grains and legumes that supply complete proteins**

**protein shakes**

## DAIRY

Dairy products like milk, cheese, and Yogurt are rich in vitamin D and calcium, which promote strong

bones and reduce the risk of osteoporosis. Choosing low-fat or fat free dairy items can help keep cholesterol levels healthy and control calorie intake.

## List of Dairy

**Yogurt and kefir fortified with vitamin D**

**Milk**

**Cheese**

**Cottage cheese**

**whey-based protein smoothies**

## Fiber

If proteins are the building blocks of the "me" machine, then fibrous carbohydrates like fruits, vegetables, and whole grains are the fuel.

# List of Recommended Fibers

Whole wheat pasta

Bread

Tortillas and crackers


fruits like Apples

Berries (all)

Cherries

Grapefrui

Kiwifruits

Nectarine

Oranges

Peaches

Pears

Plums


Oats

Beans

Brown rice

Vegetables such as potatoes (with the skins on)

Broccoli and corn

Brussels sprouts

Peas

HEALTHY FATS

Fats are essential to your health. They serve to fuel your nervous system and create your hormones. Research has shown that eating certain healthy fats can actually help burn off unwanted visceral fat (the stuff around our organs).

List of Recommended Healthy Fats

Seafood

Oils (olive, safflower, peanut, sesame)

Nuts oils

Nuts (almonds, peanuts, cashews, etc.)

Seeds (sesame, chia, flax, pumpkin)

Nut butters (all-natural, with no added oils or sugars)

Avocado and olives

## Let's Get Started...

Sometime, it's hard to keep to a routine of Dieting when you are always lost on Food to eat to keep you in line. These Over 50 Recipes we have prepared would help with the whole body reset program and will help you shrink your belly, extend your life, and create your healthiest self at mid-life and beyond.

However, if you don't like an ingredient in any of the meal, **You are free to tweak or substitute this recipes based on your personal preference,** you can substitute it with other similar ingredients, as long as it's under the Program recommendations. You can also make your own variation. The secret behind this program is to take note of the nutrients your body requires more often and look for simple, delicious ways to fit more of them into your day.

We have tried our best to bring you the best healthy meals your body needs to lose weight and burn fats , but sometimes, it's impossible to get it all right, So if you come across any error whatsoever in this book, please don't hesitate to send me a mail at Stephaniesmith@bodyReset.com. Your thoughts and feedback is important to me and it's very much welcome.

## Now on to the Recipes:

# Italian Frittata

Serves 4

**Ingredients:**

tablespoons extra-virgin olive oil

small red onion, thinly sliced

jalapeño chile, thinly sliced (ribs and seeds removed for less heat, if desired)

zucchini, thinly sliced

bunch asparagus (4 ounces), ends trimmed, tips cut into 2-inch pieces and

stalks cut into ¼-inch pieces

Coarse salt

large eggs


**How To Make it:**

1. Heat broiler. In an ovenproof skillet, heat oil over medium.
2. Add onion and jalapeño; cook, stirring, until tender, about 5 minutes.
3. Add zucchini and asparagus; cook until tender, stirring, about 7 minutes more. Season with salt.
4. Whisk eggs in a bowl; season with salt.
5. Pour into skillet with vegetables; cook, undisturbed, until sides just begin to set, 2 to 3 minutes.

6. Transfer skillet to oven; broil until frittata is just set in the middle and lightly golden and puffed on top, 2 to 3 minutes.
7. Serve warm or at room temperature.


**PER SERVING 225 CALORIES, 154 G FAT (37 G SATURATED FAT), 423 MG**

**CHOLESTEROL, 5 G CARBOHYDRATES, 14 G PROTEIN, 1 G FIBER**

# Delicious Figs with Yogurt

Serves 4

**Ingredients:**

tablespoon honey, plus more for serving (optional)

ounces fresh figs, halved

cups plain Greek yogurt

Pinch of ground cinnamon

cup chopped shelled pistachios

**How you make it:**

1. Heat honey in a skillet over medium.
2. Add figs, cut sides down, and cook until caramelized, about 5 minutes. Let cool slightly.
3. Serve over yogurt, topped with cinnamon and pistachios.
4. Drizzle with additional honey, if desired.

**PER SERVING 173 CALORIES, 6 G FAT (2 G SATURATED FAT), 8 MG CHOLESTEROL,**

**22 G CARBOHYDRATES, 12 G PROTEIN, 2 G FIBER**

# Yummy Broccoli Vinaigrette

**Servings: 6**

**What you need:**

1/2 teaspoon dry mustard

2 tablespoons white vinegar

1 teaspoon olive oil

1/4 teaspoon sea salt

1/4 teaspoon ground black pepper

1 1/2 pounds fresh broccoli

**How You Make It:**

1. Wash broccoli; lower stems and trim leaves.
2. Cut broccoli into spears. Steam until crisp-tender, for about 5 minutes. Drain.
3. Combine vinegar, pepper, oil, mustard, and sea salt.
4. Drizzle over broccoli. Serve immediately.
5. Also good chilled as cold leftovers.

# Fresh Wrapped Fish

Servings: 4

**What you need:**

3 tablespoons capers, drained

4 large stalks celery, thinly sliced

3 tablespoons fresh lemon juice

1/2 teaspoon ground black pepper

1/2 teaspoon sea salt

2 tablespoons fresh parsley

4 rectangular pieces of parchment paper

2 tablespoons dill

2 pounds fresh white fish fillets

**How You Make It:**

1. Distribute sliced celery evenly in the center of each parchment paper lay out.
2. In small bowl, mix lemon juice, capers, sea salt, parsley, pepper, and dill together.
3. Sprinkle each with a teaspoon or so of caper mix.
4. Divide fish fillets among the 4 papers.

5. Divide remaining caper mix evenly over each fillet.
6. Gather paper together in center. Fold tightly.
7. Twist ends securely to seal.
8. Bake in 400° oven for 20 minutes.
9. Packets will be slightly browned and puffed.
10. Slide packets onto dinner plates.
11. Open each Serving when you want to use.

# Steak-Fried Chicken

**Servings: 8**

**What you need:**

1 pound sliced fresh mushrooms

2 teaspoons olive oil

1 bunch scallions, chopped

1/2 teaspoon sea salt

8 boneless, skinless chicken breast

1/2 teaspoon ground black pepper

1/2 cup chicken broth

2 tablespoons chopped fresh parsley

**How You Make It:**

1. In large skillet, heat olive oil.
2. Sauté mushrooms and scallions for about 2 minutes.
3. Remove from pan. Set aside.
4. Pound chicken breasts to one-quarter-inch thickness.
5. Sprinkle with sea salt and pepper.

6. Sauté in same pan, about four minutes on each side.
7. Spread mushroom mixture over chicken breasts. Pour broth over chicken.
8. Cover, bring to a boil, and then quickly reduce heat.
9. Simmer until chicken is tender, for about 3-4 minutes.

# Apple Stew and Autumn Chicken

Serves 4

What you need:

3 carrots, peeled, sliced
1 chicken, cut in parts
1/4 cup apple cider vinegar
1/2 tsp. nutmeg
6 apples, peeled, sliced
6 whole cloves
1 cup shredded cabbage
1/2 tsp. sea salt
1/4 tsp. pepper
2 tsp. Dijon mustard
1 cup applesauce

1 3/4 cups low sodium chicken broth, warm

How You Make It:

1.  Heat large Dutch oven over medium high temperature, after spraying with vegetable cooking spray.

2.  Add chicken turning to brown on all sides, and cook, about 10 minutes.

3.  Sprinkle with nutmeg, pepper and sea salt.

4. Spread mustard over chicken pieces; add warm broth, cloves, carrots and vinegar; bring to a boil.

5. Reduce heat to low, Cover and cook 15 minutes.

6. Add apples and cook for about five minutes.

7. Add cabbage, stirring into liquid. Cook, covered, until fork can be inserted in chicken with ease, about 10 minutes more.

8. With slotted spoon, remove vegetables and chicken to warm serving bowl and keep warm.

9. Stir applesauce, into liquid; boil on high temperature for about 5 minutes and pour over chicken and vegetables.

10. Serve with brown rice, if desired.

# Scrumptious Shrimp Meal

Servings: 8

**What you need:**

3 tablespoons fresh lemon juice

1 clove garlic, grated

1/4 teaspoon cayenne pepper flakes

¼ teaspoon ground white pepper

1 medium head cabbage, grated

2 pounds medium shrimp, peeled

1/4 cup fresh lime juice

2 tablespoons chopped fresh basil leaves

1/2 teaspoon sea salt

**How You Make It:**

1. In medium bowl, stir together cayenne pepper, garlic and lemon juice.
2. Sprinkle white pepper over the top. In lemon mixture, marinate the shrimp for about 20 minutes.
3. Meanwhile, mix together the sea salt and lime juice and toss with the cabbage.

4. Cook the shrimp pan with the marinade until pink for 2 to 3 minutes.
5. Make a shallow well in the center and toss cabbage briefly.
6. Mound the shrimp in the middle of the cabbage.
7. Garnish with additional cayenne pepper flakes and basil, if desired.

# Baked Fish and Vegetables

**Servings: 8**

**What you need:**

2 cloves garlic, grated

1 head cauliflower

1 red pepper

2 green peppers

1 teaspoon crushed dried rosemary leaves

1 pound whole mushrooms

2 pound salmon fillets

2 teaspoons olive oil

1 tablespoon white vinegar

1/4 teaspoon ground black pepper

1/2 teaspoon sea salt

**How You Make It:**

1. Steam cauliflower for about a minute, after separating into florets. Drain thoroughly.
2. Cut the peppers into one-inch squares, after seeding.

3. Clean mushrooms; trim ends.
4. Combine cauliflower, mushrooms, peppers, rosemary and garlic, in a large baking dish.
5. Toss with olive oil.
6. Bake until vegetables are crisp-tender at 400° for 15-20 minutes.
7. Cut salmon into one-inch chunks.
8. Add to vegetable mixture.
9. Return to oven and bake until fish flakes easily with fork, for an additional 10-12 minutes.
10. Sprinkle fish mixture with pepper vinegar, and sea salt. Toss lightly.

# Baked Salmon and Vegetables

**Servings: 8**

What You Need:

1 pound whole mushrooms

1 head cauliflower

2 cloves garlic, grated

2 green peppers

2 teaspoons olive oil

1 red pepper

1/2 teaspoon sea salt

1 teaspoon crushed dried rosemary leaves

1/4 teaspoon ground black pepper

2 pound salmon fillets

1 tablespoon white vinegar.

How You Make It:

1. Separate the cauliflower into florets. Steam for a minute.
2. Drain thoroughly.

3. Seed peppers, cut into one-inch squares.
4. Clean mushrooms; trim ends.
5. In a large baking dish, combine peppers, mushrooms, cauliflower, rosemary and garlic.
6. Toss with olive oil. Bake at 400° for 15-20 minutes, until vegetables are crisp-tender.
7. Cut salmon into one-inch chunks.
8. Add to vegetable mixture. Return to oven and bake an additional 10-12 minutes, until fish flakes easily with fork.
9. Sprinkle fish mixture with vinegar, sea salt, and pepper. Toss lightly.

# Grilled Chicken Wraps

**Servings: 4**

**What You Need:**

Vegetable cooking spray

2 teaspoons oregano

2 tablespoons fresh lemon juice

4 thin slices peeled onion

1 green pepper, seeded and quartered

4 large lettuce leaves

1/4 cup chopped fresh mint

4 boneless, skinless chicken breast halves, rinsed, patted dry, and pounded thin

**How You Make It:**

1. Brush chicken breasts on both sides with lemon juice, after you've heated the grill.
2. Sprinkle with oregano.
3. Remove grill top and lightly coat with cooking spray. Return to grill.
4. Arrange chicken breasts and onion slices on grill. Cook, turning once, 5 to 6 minutes per side, until

chicken juices run clear when prodded with a tip of a sharp knife.

5. Onion slices and pepper quarters should take about 2 to 3 minutes per side.
6. Transfer onions and peppers to a carving board and cut into strips.
7. When chicken is done; transfer to carving board and cut into 1/2-inch strips. Keep warm.
8. Divide the chicken, pepper, and onion strips on the center of each lettuce leaf, sprinkle with mint, and roll up.
9. Secure with toothpicks if necessary.

# Grilled Lemon Salmon

**Servings: 8**

**What You Need:**

3 tablespoons lemon juice

8 salmon steaks (about 3 pounds)

1 tablespoon olive oil

3 cloves garlic, grated

1 teaspoon sea salt

1/2 teaspoon ground black pepper

**How You Make It:**

1. Mix all ingredients except salmon in a shallow glass baking dish.
2. Arrange salmon in baking dish, turning once so both sides are covered with the marinade.
3. Refrigerate for about 30 minutes. Heat grill.
4. Grill salmon until fish flakes easily with a fork, about 5 minutes per side.
5. Serve hot.

# Southwestern Scallop

**Servings: 5 main dish**

**What You Need:**

1/4 teaspoon ground black pepper

1 tablespoon dill

5 Belgian endive leaves

2/3 cup water

1/4 cup shredded Swiss cheese

2 tablespoons mayonnaise

1/2 pound bay scallops

2 tablespoons cream cheese

1 teaspoon prepared mustard

1 egg white, room temperature

**How You Make It:**

1. Dry and set aside endive leaves after washing.
2. Boil scallops until no longer translucent, in 2/3 cup water.
3. Takes about 5 minutes. Drain thoroughly and cool.

4. Cream together mayonnaise, cream cheese and Swiss cheese.
5. Stir in dill, ground black pepper and mustard. Fold in well-drained scallops.
6. Beat egg white at high speed until stiff peaks form, using an electric mixer.
7. Do not over beat.
8. Fold egg white gently into scallop mixture. Spoon scallop mixture among endive leaves.
9. Arrange in baking dish. Bake at 425° until puffy and golden for 8 to 10 minutes. Serve immediately.
10. Cut each endive leaf into 4 wedges for appetizers.

# Asparagus Chicken Salad

**Servings: 8**

**What You Need:**

1/2 pound boneless, skinless chicken breast

1/2 pound steak

2 pounds asparagus

4 hard boiled Omega-3 eggs, quartered lengthwise

1/2 pound mushrooms, sliced

1 teaspoon olive oil

4 oz. Swiss cheese

2 tablespoons finely chopped onion

1 head romaine lettuce.

**How You Make It:**

1. Poach chicken breast in small amount of water until thoroughly cooked. Drain. Cool thoroughly.
2. Cut into ½-inch strips. Set aside. Grill steak to desired doneness. Cool thoroughly.
3. Cut into ½-inch strips. Set aside. Break woody ends off asparagus. Rinse.

4. Cut into bite-sized pieces and place in a microwave-proof casserole dish.
5. Cover with plastic wrap, and microwave for 2 minutes.
6. Carefully remove plastic wrap. Plunge asparagus in cold water. Drain completely. Sauté mushrooms in 1 teaspoon olive oil for 1 minute. Remove from pan. Set aside to cool.
7. In medium glass or plastic bowl, toss cheese, chicken, steak, and onion.
8. Add asparagus and mushrooms when thoroughly cool.
9. Pour 3 tablespoons dressing over asparagus mixture. Chill for 1 hour.
10. Meanwhile, tear lettuce leaves into salad bowl. Rinse, and cover with ice water.
11. Chill while asparagus mixture is chilling.
12. Drain lettuce thoroughly. Arrange lettuce in salad bowl.
13. Pour reserved asparagus mixture over lettuce.
14. Arrange egg quarters over salad. Stir remaining dressing.
15. Serve salad with dressing.

Note: Leftover meats may be substituted for fresh cooked chicken and steak.

# Delicious Sea Scallops

**Servings: 8**

**What You Need:**

3 pounds Sea Scallops

2 tablespoons almond butter

1 1/2 pound fresh spinach

3/4 cup grated Gruyere

2 tablespoons finely chopped scallions

3/4 cup heavy cream

½ teaspoon sea salt

¼ teaspoon ground black pepper

3 large Portobello Mushrooms

**How You Make It:**

1. Sauté scallions until tender.
2. Heat One teaspoon almond butter in saucepan. Add cream.
3. When sauce begins to thicken, stirring constantly, add cheese.
4. Add pepper and sea salt to taste, keep warm.

5. Wash spinach thoroughly. Sauté spinach in half the remaining almond butter.
6. Arrange on serving plates. Clean and stem mushroom.
7. Slice mushrooms, and sauté in same pan for 1 to 2 minutes.
8. Arrange mushrooms over spinach.
9. Add remaining almond butter to pan. Sauté scallops 1 1/2 to 2 minutes on each side in same pan.
10. Arrange scallops on mushrooms. Spray reserved sauce over scallops. Serve immediately.

# Yummy Kale with chicken broth

**Servings: 4**

**What You Need:**

2 tablespoons chicken broth

1 pound kale

11/4 teaspoon sesame oil

¼ teaspoon ground black pepper

2 garlic cloves, grated

**How You Make It:**

1. Remove tough stems, after washing kale in several changes of water.
2. Cut into one-inch squares.
3. Heat the sesame oil, in a wok or frying pan.
4. Stir-fry the garlic but do not allow it to brown.
5. Add the chicken broth and kale.
6. Cover until kale wilts, for about 2-3 minutes.
7. Sprinkle with ground black pepper.

# World Greatest Egg Salad

**Servings: 4**

**What You Need:**

1/4 cup finely chopped dill pickle

8 hard boiled Omega- 3 eggs, chopped

1 teaspoon chopped fresh parsley

1/4 cup finely chopped celery

1 scallion, finely chopped1/3 cup mayonnaise

Dash pepper

1/4 teaspoon sea salt

4 large lettuce leaves

**How You Make It:**

1. Mix all the ingredients leaving only the lettuce leaves and parsley.
2. Chill. Just prior to serving, Pile on lettuce leaves.
3. Sprinkle with parsley.

# Mushroom Omelet

**Servings: 1**

**What You Need:**

2 eggs

2 cups sliced fresh mushrooms

1 teaspoon olive oil

2 tablespoons grated cheddar cheese

1 tablespoon chopped scallions

**How You Make It:**

1. Sauté mushrooms until almost ready to give up their liquid, in a little olive oil.
2. Remove from pan and set aside. Beat eggs.
3. Pour into same pan and cook over medium heat until partly solid.
4. Sprinkle with cheese, scallions and half of the mushrooms.
5. Fold over and continue cooking until hot. Top with rest of mushrooms. Serve.

# Scrambled Egg and Vegetable Wrap-ups

**Servings: 8**

**What You Need:**

1 teaspoon olive oil

2 scallions, chopped

1 tablespoon onion, chopped

1 green pepper, chopped

2 cups sliced mushrooms

8 romaine lettuce leaves

1/2 teaspoon ground black pepper

1 tablespoon taco seasoning mix, dry

4 eggs and 4 egg whites, or 8 eggs

3/4 cup shredded cheddar cheese.

**How You Make It:**

1. Coat a large skillet with olive oil. Sauté green pepper, onion, and mushrooms until tender.
2. Transfer vegetables to small bowl. Stir in scallions. Set aside.

3. On serving plates, sprinkle lettuce evenly with cheese.
4. Beat together eggs and egg whites. Stirring often, until just firm and moist, in same skillet cook eggs.
5. Divide eggs among lettuce leaves.
6. Divide vegetable mixture over eggs.
7. If necessary, roll up the lettuce leaves and secure them with toothpicks. Serve immediately.

# Over-D-Top Oven Shrimp

**Servings: 8**

**What You Need:**

1/4 teaspoon freshly ground black pepper

2 pounds large fresh shrimp, raw, deveined

2 teaspoons almond butter

2 teaspoons olive oil

2 cloves garlic, minced

1 tablespoon chopped fresh parsley

**How You Make It:**

1.  In a large bowl, combine garlic, almond butter, oil, and pepper.
2.  Add shrimp and toss lightly to coat.
3.  Spread shrimp, in a single layer, in a shallow, oven-safe casserole dish.
4.  Broil shrimp for about 3-4 minutes, approximately 4-inches from the heat.
5.  Turn shrimp, and broil for an additional 3-4 minutes (or until lightly browned).
6.  Sprinkle with chopped fresh parsley and serve.

# Shrimp and Cucumber Stir-Fry

**Servings: 4**

**What You Need:**

2 large cucumbers, peeled

3 tablespoons sunflower oil

2 tablespoons minced fresh ginger

1 clove garlic, minced

1/4 cup minced scallions

1 pound medium shrimp, shelled and deveined

Sea salt to taste

1 tablespoon white vinegar

**How You Make It:**

1. Cut cucumbers in half lengthwise; scrape out and discard seeds.
2. Cut each cucumber half crosswise into 1/4 inch thick slices.
3. Heat wok over high heat.
4. When wok is hot, add 1 tablespoon oil. When oil is hot, add cucumbers and 1 tablespoon of the ginger;

stir-fry 2-3 minutes until cucumbers are tender-crisp.

5. Arrange on serving platter. Keep warm.
6. Pour remaining oil into wok.
7. When oil is hot, add garlic, remaining 1 tablespoon ginger, scallions, and shrimp.
8. Stir-fry about 3 minutes, until shrimp is pink and cooked through.
9. Sprinkle with sea salt and pour vinegar over shrimp. Stir briefly, and arrange over cucumbers.

# Shrimp n Mushroom Stir-Fry

**Servings: 4**

**What You Need:**

2 cups sliced mushrooms

1 teaspoon sesame oil

1 teaspoon olive oil

1 clove garlic, grated

1/2 teaspoon grated fresh ginger

1 cup okra

1/2 cup chopped green peppers

2 cups string beans

1/4 teaspoon ground black pepper

2 cups cleaned cooked shrimp

**How You Make It:**

1. Combine and Heat Stir-fry mushrooms, garlic, peppers, and ginger in sesame oil and olive oil until crisp-tender.
2. Meanwhile string beans and steam okra until crisp-tender.

3. Drain, and add to peppers and mushrooms.
4. Stir in shrimp and pepper until just warmed.
5. Serve over a bed of lettuce.

# Spinach n Chicken Salad

**Servings: 8**

**What You Need:**

1/2 pound fresh sliced mushrooms

1/2 pound fresh spinach

4 cups cooked, diced chicken

2 tablespoons olive oil

3 tablespoons white vinegar

1/2 teaspoon poppy seeds

1/4 teaspoon dry mustard

**How You Make It:**

1. In small bowl, combine vinegar, mustard, oil, and poppy seeds together.
2. Refrigerate.
3. Wash spinach and tear into bite size pieces.
4. Add mushrooms and chicken. Serve.

## Orange Glazed Chicken Wings

**Serves 2**

**What you need:**

1 tbsp. vegetable oil

18 chicken wings, tips removed and wings cut in half at joint

1/2 cup orange marmalade

1/4 cup Dijon mustard

2 tbsp. soy sauce

**How you make it:**

1. Heat the oil in a large skillet over mediu m-high heat.
2. Add the wing pieces, and fry until golde n brown on all sides, about 6 to 10 minut es.
3. Spoon off any excess fat, and add the ora nge marmalade, mustard and soy sauce to the skillet, stirring to bl

end the ingredients and coat the wing pi
eces.
4. Simmer on medium heat 8 to 10 minute
s, until
the sauce thickens and glazes the wings.
5. Serve hot.

## Serves 4

## What you need:

12 eggs

1 1/2 cups milk, divided

1/2 teaspoon sea salt

1/4 teaspoon pepper

2 tbsp. diced pimientos

2 tbsp. minced fresh parsley or chives

2 tbsp. all-purpose flour

1/4 cup almond butter or margarine

## How you make it

1. In a large bowl, beat eggs and 1 cup milk
   .
2. Add the sea
   salt, pepper, pimientos and parsley.

3. In a small bowl, combine flour and rema
ining
milk until smooth; stir into egg mixture.
4. In a large skillet, melt almond butter
over medium heat.
5. Add egg mixture.
6. Cook and stir over medium heat until th
e eggs are completely set.

Avocado Kale Salad

**Yield: 2 servings**

**Ingredients:**

½ cucumber, sliced

1 handful **almonds**

½ head of **kale**

1 **avocado**

1 handful radishes, sliced

Sea sea salt, to taste

½ lemon, squeezed for juice

**How you make it:**

1. Sauté (toss) the kale and avocado, using your hands.
2. Then add the radishes, cucumbers, and almonds.
3. Finally toss the salad with lemon juice and sea sea salt.

## Ingredients:

1 ounce feta cheese, crumbled

2 (6 ounce) fillets salmon

1/4 cup Almond butter, melted and divided
sea salt and pepper to taste

4 ounces fresh mushrooms, sliced

12 grape tomatoes, halved

2 tbsp. olive oil, divided

5 sprigs fresh cilantro, chopped

8 ounces leaf lettuce, torn into bite-size pieces

1 avocado - peeled, pitted, and cubed

1 fresh jalapeno pepper, chopped

2 tbsp. distilled white vinegar

## How you make it:

1. Preheat the oven broiler.
2. Line a baking sheet with aluminum foil.

3. Place the salmon on the foil, and brush with 2 tbsp. melted almond butter.
4. Season with sea salt and pepper.
5. Broil 15 minutes, until fish is easily flaked with a fork.
6. Melt the remaining almond butter in a skillet over medium heat, and sauté the mushrooms until tender.
7. Place the tomatoes in a bowl, and drizzle with 1 tbsp. olive oil.
8. Season with sea salt and pepper.
9. Toss together the mushrooms, avocado, salmon, tomatoes, lettuce, cilantro, and jalapeno, in a large bowl.
10. Pour small amount of the remaining olive oil and the vinegar over the surface.
11. Add sea salt and pepper Seasoning to taste, and spread with feta cheese to serve.

**Serves 4**

**Ingredients:**

1 1/2 tbsp. fresh lime juice

2 fluid ounces rum

1 tbsp. brown sugar

1/4 teaspoon cayenne pepper

1/4 teaspoon ground clove

1/2 teaspoon ground cinnamon

1/2 teaspoon ground ginger

1 teaspoon black pepper

1/2 teaspoon sea salt

1/2 teaspoon dried thyme leaves

1 (3 pound) whole chicken

1 tbsp. vegetable oil

**How you make it:**

1. Preheat oven to 325 º F (165 º C).
2. In a small bowl, combine the lime juice, rum, and brown sugar; set aside.
3. Mix together the cayenne pepper, clove, cinnamon, ginger, pepper, sea salt, and thyme leaves.
4. Brush the chicken with oil, then coat wit h the spice mixture.
5. Place in a roasting pan, and bake about 90 minutes, until the juices run clear or until a meat thermometer in serted in thickest part of the thigh reaches 180 º F.
6. Baste the chicken with the sauce every 2 0 minutes while it's cooking. Allow chick en to rest for 10 minutes before carving.

## Curried Chicken Salad

**Ingredients:**

3 cups diced cooked chicken breast meat

6 slices bacon

1/2 cup chopped celery

1 cup seedless grapes

1 cup mayonnaise

2 tbsp. red onion, minced

1/2 tsp. curry powder

1 tsp lemon juice

1/2 tsp. Worcestershire sauce

Sea salt and pepper to taste.


**How you make it:**


1. In a large, deep skillet, place bacon. Cook until evenly brown over medium high heat.
2. Crumble and set aside.

3. Combine bacon, chicken, celery, and grapes, in a large bowl.
4. Prepare the dressing in a small bowl by whisking together the lemon juice,
5. mayonnaise, onion, Worcestershire sauce, curry and
6. Sea

   salt and pepper. Pour over salad and toss well.

**Serves 4**

**What you need:**

1 (12 inch) pre-baked pizza crust

1/2 cup pesto basil sauce

2 cups cooked chicken breast strips

1/2 cup shredded fontina cheese.

1 (6 ounce) jar artichoke hearts, drained

**Directions:**

1. Preheat the oven to 450 ° F (230 ° C).

2. Spread pesto sauce over the pizza crust
   .

3. Arrange chicken pieces and artichoke h earts over the sauce, and sprinkle with c heese.

4. Bake for 8 to 10 minute in the preheate d oven, until cheese is melted and lightly browned at the edges.

## What you need:

1 tbsp. vegetable oil

1 (10 ounce) can refrigerated pizza crust

1 1/2 cups shredded Mexican blend cheese, divided.

1 medium onion, chopped

1 garlic clove, minced

1/2 cup finely chopped zucchini

1 (15 ounce) can black beans, rinsed and drained

1 (14.5 ounce) can Italian diced tomatoes, undrained

## How you make it:

1.   Press dough into a greased 15-in. x 10-in. x 1-in. baking pan. Bake at 425 ° F for 4-6 minutes or until crust just begins to brown.

2.   Meanwhile, in a skillet, saute the onion and garlic in oil until tender.

3. Add zucchini; cook and stir for 1 minut e. Add the beans and tomatoes; bring to a boil. Boil, uncovered, for 2 minutes; dr ain.

4. Sprinkle 2/3 cup of cheese over crust.

5. Top with bean mixture and remaining c heese. Bake 8-
10 minutes longer or until crust is brown ed and cheese is melted.

# Ultimate Fried Eggs

**Serves 2**

**What you need:**

4 Free-range eggs

1 Tablespoon nut almond butter

½ Teaspoon sea salt

1/8 Teaspoon marjoram

1/8 Teaspoon pepper

½ Teaspoon parsley

2 Teaspoons red wine vinegar

**How you prepare it:**

1. Break the free-range eggs into skillet over half Tablespoon melted almond butter.
2. Add spices and cook until whites are solid.
3. Place eggs onto serving plates.
4. Heat for two minutes, after melting remaining half Tablespoon of almond butter.
5. Stir in red wine vinegar and allow mixture to cook for another minute.
6. Pour over eggs.
7. Garnish with parsley and serve.

# Lime Broiled Catfish

**Serves 2**

**What you need:**

1/4 teaspoon pepper

1 tablespoon margarine

2 tablespoons lime juice

2 catfish fillets (6 ounces each)

1/4 teaspoon garlic powder

**How you prepare it:**

1. In a saucepan, melt margarine.
2. Stir in pepper, lime juice and garlic powder; mix well.
3. Remove from heat and set aside.
4. In a shallow baking dish, place fillets.
5. Brush each generously with lime sauce.
6. Broil until fish flakes easily with a fork or for about 5-8 minutes.
7. Remove to a warm serving dish; spoon pan juices over each fillet.

# Pumpkin and Shrimp

**Serves 6**

**What you need**

1 2-3 lbs. pumpkin

2 lbs. medium shrimp

3 cloves garlic

2 large yellow onions, chopped

2 bunches cilantro

4 large plum tomatoes

Tabasco Sauce, to taste

Olive oil for sautéing

Sea salt and pepper

**How you prepare it:**

1. Line a roasting pan with heavy foil.
2. Preheat oven to 350.
3. Slice off top of pumpkin and save to use as cover/lid.
4. Take out pumpkin strings and seeds.

5.  Sauté chopped onions till translucent and beginning to caramelize in the olive oil.
6.  Chop and add garlic to the onions.
7.  Add freshly ground pepper and sea salt.
8.  Clean and devein shrimp.
9.  Chop tomatoes and sauté with garlic and onions till the tomatoes have softened.
10. Add shrimp and sauté until shrimp turn pink.
11. Ensure not to overcook!! Chop the cilantro and sprinkle over the shrimp mixture.
12. Taste for sea salt and pepper.
13. Fill the pumpkin with the shrimp mixture. Cover with lid.
14. Bake until the pumpkin is soft. Dish out pumpkin and shrimp together.

# Brown's Simple but Delicious Fish

**Serves 2**

**What you need:**

1 tsp. dried dill

2 Rainbow trout or salmon fillets

1 tbsp. coarse brown mustard

## 1/2 cup heavy cream

**How you prepare it:**

1. Mix mustard, cream, and dill.
2. Pour over fish and bake for 20-30 minutes (depending on thickness of fish), in 375 degree oven until fish is just flaky in center.
3. Do not overcook!

# Crunchy Vegetables with Chicken

**Serves 4**

**What you need:**

1 teaspoon dark sesame oil

3/4 pound skinned, boned chicken breast, cut into 1-inch pieces

1/4 cup low-sodium teriyaki sauce, divided

1 cup diagonally sliced celery

1 clove garlic, crushed

3/4 cup thinly sliced carrot

1 (8-ounce) can sliced water chestnuts, drained

1 cup coarsely shredded red cabbage

**How you prepare it:**

1. In a bowl, combine chicken and 1 tablespoon teriyaki sauce; stir well.
2. Let stand 10 minutes.
3. Heat oil in a nonstick skillet over medium-high heat. Add carrot, celery, and garlic; stir-fry 1 minute.

4. Stir in cabbage and water chestnuts; remove from skillet.
5. Add chicken; stir-fry 3 minutes. Add remaining teriyaki sauce; stir-fry 1 minute.
6. Return cabbage mixture to skillet; stir-fry 1 minute or until done.
7. Yield: 4 servings (serving size: 1 cup).

# Balsamic Pepper Chicken

**Serves 4**

**What you need:**

2 tsp. Extra-virgin olive oil

4 boneless skinless chicken breasts

1/3 cup balsamic vinegar

2 tsp. lemon pepper

2 cloves garlic, minced

1/4 cup chicken stock


**How you prepare it:**


1. On both sides of the chicken, sprinkle lemon pepper.
2. Heat oil over medium heat, in a skillet.
3. Add chicken and cook until chicken is no longer pink inside, or for about 5-7 minutes on each side.
4. Remove chicken to a serving platter and keep it warm.
5. Mix broth, vinegar, and garlic and add to the skillet.
6. Stir cook over medium-high heat until the mixture is reduced and slightly thickened, or for about 2 minutes. Pour sauce over chicken breasts and serve.

Tip: You can double the sauce ingredients if you want extra sauce for dipping.

# Mushroom Chicken

**Serves 6**

**What you need:**

12 chicken thighs
Paprika

Sea salt and Pepper


*Sauce:*
1/2 pound mushrooms, sliced

1/4 cup almond butter

3/4 cup whipping cream

1 tbsp. almond flour

1 tsp. soy sauce


**How you prepare it:**

1. Preheat oven to 350 F.
2. On a rack over a large cookie sheet, place chicken thighs.
3. Season with sea salt and pepper to taste. Generously dust with paprika.
4. Bake for 1 hr. To make sauce, melt almond butter in large skillet.

5. Add mushrooms; sprinkle with flour, toss mushrooms to distribute flour.
6. Sauté over medium heat, stirring occasionally for 8 to 10 minutes.
7. Add soy sauce, and slowly stir in cream.
8. Cook and stir till mixture bubbles and thickens.
9. Season to taste with sea salt and pepper.
10. Serve over baked chicken thighs.

# Chicken Parmesan

**Serves 4**

**What you need:**

## 1 egg, slightly beaten

4 boneless and skinless chicken breast halves

1/2 cup crushed pork rinds

1/2 cup tomato sauce

2 tbsp. Almond butter

1/2 cup Shredded mozzarella cheese

1/4 cup Chopped fresh parsley

1 tbsp. Grated Parmesan cheese

**How you prepare it:**

1.  Flatten chicken to even thickness, using palm of hand.
2.  Dip chicken into egg then into crumbs to coat.
3.  In skillet over medium heat, in hot margarine, brown chicken on both sides.
4.  Add tomato sauce. Reduce heat. Cover; simmer 10 minutes.
5.  Sprinkle with cheeses and parsley. Cover; simmer until cheese melts, about 5 minutes.

# Almond Chicken Salad

**Serves 4-6**

**What you need:**

4 cups cubed cooked chicken
1 cup chopped celery
1 1/2 cups seedless green grapes
3/4 cup sliced green onion
3 free-range eggs, chopped
1/2 cup almond butter
1/2 tsp. pepper
1/4 cup sour cream
1 Tbsp. prepared mustard
1 tsp. sea salt
1/4 tsp. onion pepper
1/4 tsp. celery sea salt
1/8 tsp. dry mustard
1/8 tsp. paprika
1 kiwifruit, peeled and sliced (optional)
1/2 cup slivered almonds, toasted

**How you prepare it:**

1. Combine grapes, celery, onions, chicken, and eggs, in large bowl.

2. Combine the other nine ingredients, in another bowl; stir until smooth.

3. Pour over chicken mixture and toss gently.

4.  Stir in almonds and serve immediately, or refrigerate and add almonds right before serving.

5.  Garnish with kiwifruit if desired.

## Smoky Salmon Spread

**Serves 4**

**What you need:**

2 8-oz packages cream cheese

2 6-oz cans boneless, skinless pink salmon

3 Tbs. lemon juice

1 tsp. dill weed

3 Tbs. cream

3-4 drops liquid smoke flavoring

Pork skins

1/4 cup green onions

**How you prepare it:**

1. Drain salmon. Beat cream cheese with lemon juice, cream and dill weed in mixer until light and fluffy.
2. Beat in green onions and salmon until thoroughly combined.
3. Season with liquid smoke to taste.
4. Before serving, chill several hours to allow flavors to blend.
5. Spread on pork skins, to serve.

# Macadamia Nut Chicken

**Serves 4**

**What you need:**

1 free-range egg

4-6 chicken or fish cutlets

1 cup Macadamia nut crumbs

1/2 cup Macadamia nut oil (or an olive oil/almond butter combination)

2 tbsp. lemon juice

Fresh chopped parsley

Sea salt and pepper

**How you prepare it:**

1. Dry the roll and cutlets in seasoned flour.
2. Cover cutlets with beaten free-range egg and roll in Macadamia nut crumbs.
3. Heat oil in pan and fry cutlets gently until light brown either side.
4. Add lemon juice and continue cooking for 5 minutes.
5. Serve garnished with parsley.

# Sesame Green Beans

**Serves 6**

**What you need:**

3/4 pound fresh green beans

1/2 cup water

1 Tablespoon Almond butter

1 Tablespoon soy sauce

2 teaspoons of sesame seeds, toasted

**How you prepare it:**

1. In a saucepan, bring beans and water to a boil; reduce heat to medium.
2. Cover and cook until the beans are crisp-tender, for about 10-15 minutes; drain.
3. Add soy sauce, almond butter, and sesame seeds; toss to coat.

# Tasty Chicken Egg Foo Young

**Serves 4**

**What you need:**

1 cup shredded string beans

8 eggs

I cup sliced mushrooms, canned or fresh

I cup shredded celery

1 1/2 cups shredded cooked chicken

Sea salt and pepper to taste

1 cup shredded onions

**How you make it:**

1.  Place all ingredients in a mixing bowl, combine them thoroughly and divide into 8 portions.

2.  Grease well a hot skillet; fry both sides until golden brown.

**Serves 2**

**What you need:**

4 eggs

1 Tablespoon almond butter

1/8 Teaspoon pepper

½ Teaspoon Sea salt

1/8 Teaspoon marjoram

½ Teaspoon parsley

2 Teaspoons red wine vinegar

**How you make it:**

1. Break eggs into skillet over ½ Tablespoon melted almond butter.
2. Add spices and cook until whites are solid.
3. On your serving plates, place eggs.
4. Melt remaining ½ Tablespoon of almond butter and heat for 2 min.

5. Allow mixture to cook for another minute, after stirring in red wine vinegar.
6. Pour over eggs. Garnish with parsley.

## Serves 12

Ginger, onion and garlic are blended in the coating for this easy baked chicken. Yogurt helps keep it moist.

## What you need:

1 cup soft bread crumbs
2 fresh whole chickens, cut up
1/2 tsp. onion powder
1/4 tsp. cayenne pepper
1/2 tsp. garlic powder
1/8 tsp. ground ginger
1/3 cup plain yogurt

## How you make it:

1.  Preheat oven to 350°F.

2.  Lightly spray a medium baking dish with vegetable cooking spray; set aside.

3.  Rinse chicken pieces and pat dry.

4.  Combine bread crumbs, garlic powder, onion powder, cayenne pepper and ginger, in a shallow bowl.

5.   Dip chicken pieces in yogurt, then into crumb mixture.

6.    Place in prepared dish. Bake, uncovered, until chicken is tender or for about 45 to 50 minutes.

## Shrimp Stir-Fry

**Servings: 4**

**What you need:**

1 teaspoon sesame oil

1 teaspoon olive oil

1 clove garlic, grated

2 cups sliced mushrooms

1/2 teaspoon grated fresh ginger

1 cup okra

1/2 cup chopped green peppers

2 cups string beans

1/4 teaspoon ground black pepper

2 cups cleaned cooked shrimp

**How you make it:**

1. Stir-fry peppers, mushrooms, garlic, and ginger in olive oil and sesame oil until crisp-tender.
2. Meanwhile steam okra and string beans until crisp-tender.

3. Drain, and add to mushrooms and peppers. Stir in shrimp and pepper until just warmed.
4. Serve over a bed of lettuce. Enjoy!

# Southern Mushroom Soup

Servings: 4

## What you need:

1/2 cups chopped fresh mushrooms

1 small onion, chopped

1/2 cups chicken broth

1/2 tablespoons almond butter, melted

1 tablespoons all-purpose flour

1/2 cups milk

1/8 cup heavy cream

1 pinch sea salt and pepper to taste

2 slices white bread, toasted

1/4 tablespoon softened almond butter

1/4 cup shredded sharp Cheddar cheese.

## How you make it:

1.  In a saucepan, combine the mushrooms, onion and chicken broth.

2. Bring to a boil, then simmer covered for 15 minutes over low heat.
3. Stir together the melted almond butter and flour to make a paste.
4. Stir the paste into the pan with the vegetables.
5. Increase the heat to medium, and gradually stir in the milk.
6. Continue stirring constantly.
7. When the mixture thickens and begins to boil, stir in the cream.
8. Cook over low heat without boiling for about 10 minutes, or until the mushrooms are tender.
9. Season with sea salt and pepper.
10. Ladle the soup into bowls, and trim pieces of toast to fit the bowls.
11. Almond butter the toast, and place on top of the soup.
12. Sprinkle the cheese over the bread and serve.

# Thai Chicken Salad

This salad is great with either tuna or chicken. If your taste buds cannot handle chili, use less or leave it out altogether.

**Servings: 2**

## What you need:

2 lettuce leaves (use different kinds)

1/2 tbsp. coriander, chopped

1/2 tbsp. fresh mint, chopped

1/4 orange, peeled and sectioned

1/4 can tuna or 1 chicken breast, cooked and shredded

100 g red seedless grapes, halved

1/8 cucumber, sliced

1/2 small red onion, thinly sliced

## Dressing

Zest of 1 lime

Juice of 1 limes

1 garlic cloves

1/2 serrano chilies, halved, seeded and cut into pieces

1/2 tbsp. fish or soy sauce

2 tbsp. cashews, chopped

1/2 tbsp. honey or agave nectar

## How you make it:

1.  Place half the lettuce in a bowl or on a platter. Tear the rest of the lettuce leaves into bite sizes and add to the bowl or platter.
2.  Sprinkle the coriander and mint over the lettuce leaves.
3.  Add the orange, tuna or chicken, grapes, cucumber and red onion.
4.  Refrigerate this while you make the dressing.
5.  Grate the lime zest into a blender or food processor.
6.  Add the garlic, chilies, lime juice, fish or soy sauce and honey or agave, and blend until smooth.
7.  Pour the dressing over the salad. Garnish with cashews and serve.

# Fish with Mediterranean Salsa

**Servings: 2**

## What you need:

1 tsp. extra virgin olive oil

1/2 tsp. dried oregano

2 fish fillets

1 tbsp. water

1/4 tsp. chili powder

1/2 tsp. dried thyme

1/2 tsp. freshly grated lemon zest

1/2 tomato, deseeded and chopped

1/2 (60g) can Kalamata olives or ripe olives, drained and sliced

5 g fresh parsley, chopped

Juice of ½ lemon

1/2 tbsp. capers, drained (optional)

## How you make it:

1. Preheat the oven to 160°C or Gas Mark 3.

2. Coat a baking dish with cooking oil spray and arrange the fish in a single layer.

3. Pour the water over the fish and sprinkle with chili powder, thyme and lemon zest. Cover the dish with foil and bake for 15 minutes.

4. Mix the tomato, olives, lemon juice, parsley, capers, oil and oregano thoroughly, in a small bowl.

5. Place the fish on a serving platter, top with the salsa and serve.

# Slow Cooker Chicken Curry with Quinoa

**Servings: 1-2**

## What you need:

1/3 cup quinoa

1 1/2 pounds diced chicken breast meat

1 1/4 cups chopped celery

1 3/4 cups chopped Granny Smith apples

3/4 cup chopped onion

1 cup chicken broth

1/4 cup nonfat milk

1 tablespoon curry powder

1/4 teaspoon paprika

## How you make it:

1.  Place the chicken, onion, celery, apple, chicken broth, milk, curry powder, and paprika into a slow cooker; stir until mixed.
2.  Cover, and cook on Low for 4 to 5 hours.
3.  Stir in the quinoa during the final 35 minutes of cooking.
4.  Serve when quinoa is tender

# Quinoa Pudding with Vanilla

**Servings: 2**

## What you need:

1/2 cup quinoa, rinsed

1/8 cup natural cane sugar

1/8 teaspoon ground cardamom

1 cups almond or hemp milk

1/4 cup water

1 teaspoons vanilla extract

Fine sea salt to taste

## How you make it:

1. In a medium saucepan, add the quinoa, sugar, cardamom, sea salt, milk, and water over medium heat.
2. Allow the ingredients to reach a boil and then reduce the heat to medium-low.
3. Cover the saucepan with the lid slightly ajar.
4. Simmer the pudding for approximately 30 minutes, stirring occasionally.

5. The quinoa should become very soft and the mixture should have a thick consistency.
6. Remove the quinoa from the heat and stir in the vanilla.
7. Put the pudding in a heatproof bowl and allow it to cool until it reaches room temperature.

# Quinoa with Almond Porridge

Servings: 2

## What you need:

1 ¼ cups soy or almond milk, divided

½ cup quinoa, rinsed

1 cup water

½ teaspoon ground cinnamon

Drizzle of honey

Dried or fresh fruit, for serving

Pinch of sea sea salt

## How you make it:

1. Over medium heat, place a medium saucepan.
2. Add the quinoa and cook.
3. Stir the quinoa for a few minutes until it is toasted.
4. Add 1 cup of the milk, cinnamon, the water, and sea sea salt.
5. Stir the mixture and turn up the heat until it begins to boil.

6. Reduce the heat to low, once the quinoa is boiling.
7. Cook for approximately 25 minutes, while the saucepan is covered.
8. Stir the porridge occasionally until it becomes thick and the quinoa is tender.
9. Drizzle the remaining milk and honey over the porridge and add the fruit before serving.

# The 7 Key Secrets to Achieving Your Maximum Weight-loss in This Program.

1. **practice mindful eating:** It's easy to allow your daily intake of food to become more

routine than ritual. Instead, slow down and savor every bite— without any distractions. Because when you take the time to focus on what's in front of you, something wonderful happens: You begin to feel more satisfied with less.

2. **engage in an active lifestyle:** With so much attention being paid to how (and what) you eat, it makes sense to focus on how much you move, too. This is less about committing to a rigorous workout routine and more about taking part in the types of activities that boost your energy, improve your mood, and leave you feeling better than you did before.

**4. make sure to get enough fiber:** Fiber is absolutely essential to good health: It aids in digestion, regulates blood sugar, promotes a healthy heart, and helps to control weight. Fiber also feeds the good bacteria in the digestive tract, which invariably helps the immune system protect against invading pathogens (unfriendly bacteria and viruses) and escorts toxins out of the body.

**5. boost energy with lean protein:** Protein provides us with the necessary fuel to power us through

the day, promotes brain functioning, and keeps us sated. It's also necessary for building muscles, bones, and cartilage, and every cell in our body needs protein for maintenance and repair. Most Americans (and even vegans) have no problem getting enough protein, but the source of the protein also matters.

**6. pay attention to how you feel:** Food allergies are rare, affecting only 3 to 4 percent of adults in the United States. Yet food intolerances are on the rise, with many Americans experiencing sensitivities to one or more types of food. Though far less severe than allergies, sensitivities can negatively impact your digestive health as well as your quality of life.

**7. remember to stay hydrated:** Water is crucial to our well-being: It makes up about 60 percent of our bodies, and every system depends on it. Water carries nutrients to cells, moistens membranes, cushions and protects joints and organs, regulates body temperature, keeps the digestive tract working smoothly, and helps flush out toxins and waste. The need to stay hydrated is a simple concept, yet there are plenty of questions—and some controversy—about just how to do so.

**Bonus: know what you are buying:** Understanding what grocery-store buzzwords mean—and what they don't mean—is essential for establishing good shopping habits.

# Thank You

If you follow religiously to The <u>WHOLE BODY RESET</u>. And some of the clean meal provided for you in this book. You are going to be seeing great results in your body and health, because you would lose weight and keep it off for good.

**<u>If you enjoyed the recipes in this book, please take the time to share your thoughts and post a positive review with 5 star rating on Amazon, it would encourage me and make me serve you better. It'd be greatly appreciated!</u>**

Made in the USA
Las Vegas, NV
02 April 2022

46744682R00056